HARRY'S HIDEOUT

The Big Splash
Spot the Difference

Rebecca Parkinson

CWR

Harry's Hideout
SPOT THE DIFFERENCE

Down at the bottom of the garden, behind the shed and hidden deep within the bushes, is Harry's favourite place in the world – his Hideout. It is cosy and dry and crammed full with all his greatest treasures. Harry and Grandad built the Hideout together. On the day it was finished Grandad presented Harry with a special book to store amongst his treasures.

'Harry,' he said, 'we have made a wonderful Hideout, but this book will teach you about the One who made the whole of the universe! Read it often.'

It was then that the adventures began …

Harry wanted to pretend that he hadn't heard his mum shouting to him from upstairs. He looked round hoping to spot some way of escape, but it was no use. His big brother Joshua was watching him and he was sure to tell Mum if Harry were to run off now.

'Harry!' The voice was getting louder. 'Harry, come here immediately and clear up this mess in your bedroom!'

Harry walked slowly up the stairs; sometimes it felt like he didn't do anything right! It didn't take Harry long to tidy his room and he wandered back downstairs, hoping that Mum wouldn't notice the pile of things he had stuffed under the bed.

Joshua was reading at the kitchen table and Harry peered over his shoulders. On the open page there were two pictures.

'What are you doing?' Harry asked. 'Why are there two pictures that look exactly the same?'

'Can't you read?' Joshua said crossly, pointing to the words above the pictures. 'It says "Spot the Difference". There are ten little things that are different in the two pictures. You have to find all of them.'

Harry fumbled in his pocket and pulled out the magnifying glass that had been a free gift on the front of his favourite comic earlier in the week.

'Can I help?' he asked. 'I can use this!'

Joshua rolled his eyes. 'You're not old enough,' he said, in the voice that always made Harry feel sad. 'You wouldn't be any help. Why don't you ask Mum if you can play out?'

Sadly Harry put on his coat, pushed his feet into his wellies and pulled his woolly hat down over his ears. He wished he wasn't always in trouble and that he could be clever like Joshua. It was a cold damp autumn morning but Mum had said he could play outside as long as he was wrapped up warm. Harry couldn't help but feel that she was glad of some peace and quiet.

'I know,' he said to himself. 'I'll see what different things I can spot in the garden!'

Harry soon found a large black slug leaving a shiny trail behind itself on the pathway. Through the magnifying glass he could see the beautiful markings on its body and the antennae which became bigger and smaller as it moved along.

Next Harry found a snail on the underside of a bucket near the sand pit; he studied it carefully noticing the beautiful spiral shape and the different shades of brown on the shell. Harry put the slug and snail next to each other. In some ways they looked very similar but in other ways they were completely different.

Harry wandered across to the cherry blossom tree in the corner of the garden. In the springtime this was a mass of pink flowers but now it was totally different.

'Wow!' he whispered, gazing at the mixture of red, orange, green and yellow leaves on the ground. 'I didn't know there were so many colours!'

Harry looked at each leaf in turn, becoming more and more amazed. Even though all the leaves had fallen from the same tree Harry couldn't spot any leaves that were exactly the same as each other.

Suddenly Harry had an idea. He quickly collected a huge pile of leaves from the ground and ran towards his Hideout. It looked dark and dreary inside but Harry didn't want to turn on the light until he had carried out his plan. Taking one leaf at a time Harry arranged the leaves on the floor of the Hideout, until the whole area was covered. Then he reached up to switch on the torch that hung from a nail in the ceiling. At once the Hideout filled with light.

Harry gazed at the carpet he had created. It was beautiful. The torchlight reflected off the different colours making them appear even more spectacular than they had in the garden. Harry sat down on his beanbag and looked around. He didn't think he had ever seen the Hideout look so warm and cosy; he felt like a king in his palace. At least in here no one could tell him off!

Harry pulled a thick camouflage blanket round his shoulders and lifted Grandad's book down off the shelf. Slowly he opened the book and began to read …

Suddenly the Hideout began to spin. Harry felt tingles running through his body. He shut his eyes tight. This had happened before … Where would he end up this time?

When Harry opened his eyes he found that he was seated with his back against a large rock on a stony beach. He was wearing a faded brown tunic and his feet were bare. It was night time but Harry could hear voices murmuring softly close by and he peeped over the rock to see who was speaking.

By the light of the camp fire Harry counted twelve men. He leaned forward hoping to hear what they were saying.

'Well, if we are going to be Jesus' disciples,' he heard one man say, 'we should find out a bit about each other. After all we are rather a funny mixture of people! So what about you, Peter? Why don't you go first? Tell us about how you became a follower of Jesus.'

The man called Peter cleared his throat.

'Well, early one morning,' he began, 'I was cleaning my fishing net with my brother, Andrew and our friends, James and John. I looked up and saw Jesus walking along the beach. There were crowds of people all round Him, pushing and shoving as they tried to get closer to Him. But He came straight up to me and asked if I'd mind rowing Him a little way out from the shore so He could talk to the people from there.

'So I immediately helped Him into the boat and Jesus began to speak to the crowds. As soon as He'd finished I thought He'd want to go back onto dry land. But instead He said to me, "Row out into a deeper part of the lake and cast your net back into the water."

'Well, I thought that was really silly! We'd already been out fishing all night and we hadn't even caught one fish! But for some reason I decided to do what He said. So we rowed out further into the lake, put our nets in the water and suddenly …

'"HELP!"

'I had to shout to the men in the other boat to come and rescue us. We'd caught so many fish that I thought the boat was going to sink!

'In the end both boats were full to overflowing. None of us had ever seen anything like it! I remember rowing back to the shore full of amazement. Suddenly our lives were changed! We left our jobs as fishermen and followed Jesus.'

Peter glanced round at the group.

'Now it's your turn, Matthew,' he said, turning to a man on his left. 'Tell us your story; I was there when Jesus asked you to follow Him. It was a bit of a surprise!'

Matthew smiled.

'It was a surprise to me too,' he said. 'I'd never been very popular since the day I started work as a tax collector. It was our job to collect money from people and give it to the Roman leaders, but most of us charged far more than we should have done and kept all the extra for ourselves – it was an easy way to become rich!

'Then one day I was sitting at my table ordering people to give me their money, when Jesus walked over and said, "Matthew, follow me!"

'The strange thing was, I didn't really need to think about it. I was so happy that a man like Jesus didn't just think of me as bad and push me away from Him. Instead He wanted me to be His friend. So I got up straight away, left all my riches behind me and have followed Him ever since.'

A loud laugh from Peter made Harry jump.

'Do you remember how cross some people were when Jesus and the rest of us went back to your house for a meal?' he asked.

Matthew nodded.

'They were furious!' he said. 'They thought Jesus should only bother with good people. But Jesus made it clear how important even people like me are to Him.'

'And people like me,' added a young man, seated furthest away from the fire.

'And me,' added another quietly. 'All of us so different from each other but all of us so special to Him!'

The group of men were quiet for a moment, as if they were all wondering why Jesus had chosen them to be His special friends.

Harry was just wondering who would be the next to speak when suddenly he felt tingles running through his body. Things began to spin. He shut his eyes tight …

When Harry opened his eyes he was back in his Hideout, Grandad's book resting on his knee. He felt quite disappointed that he hadn't stayed to hear everyone's story. He quietly repeated the words he had heard Matthew say: 'All of us so different from each other but all of us so special to Him.'

Suddenly Harry found that he understood something he had never realised before. It didn't matter that he was different to Joshua. It didn't matter that sometimes he got things wrong and that he wasn't as clever as some people. God had made him as he was and he was different to everyone else in the whole world, but that was what made him special. Harry found that he was smiling.

'Harry?' Joshua's head popped round the door of the Hideout. He stopped and looked in amazement at the leafy carpet.

'Wow!' he said. 'Have you done this? It looks stunning!'

Harry nodded.

'I'd never think of doing anything like this,' Joshua continued. 'You have such a good imagination! Stay here a minute.'

Joshua ran up the garden path and returned a few minutes later with Mum carrying a tray of drinks and biscuits.

'Joshua says we should eat in here,' Mum explained. 'He says it's the nicest room in the house. And at least it's not got a bed that you can stuff things under!'

Why not read about the disciples in your own Bible? You will find the stories about Peter and Matthew in Bible books Luke, chapter 5 verses 1–11 and Matthew, chapter 9 verses 9–13.

Have a go!

Have a look round your garden or in the park and see if you can collect leaves of different colours. If it is autumn there will be lots of lovely bright colours. If it is springtime or summer the colours may not be as bright, but you will be able to find lots of different shades of green. Check with an adult before you pick leaves!

You will need:

White material (a cut up white t-shirt is fine), a small stone (or a small hammer if there is an adult who will help you), and leaves. (This activity also works with flowers such as buttercups.)

What to do:

Place a leaf onto one side of the white material and fold the opposite side over the top so the leaf is sandwiched in the middle.

Now carefully knock the stone (or hammer) onto the material so the leaf beneath it is lightly squashed. As you do this you will see the colour from the leaf making a leaf pattern on the material.

The more you bash the leaf, the more colour you will see! Once you have practised the technique it will be possible to make pictures using different leaves and flowers.

Harry's Hideout
THE BIG SPLASH

Down at the bottom of the garden, behind the shed and hidden deep within the bushes, is Harry's favourite place in the world – his Hideout. It is cosy and dry and crammed full with all his favourite possessions. Harry and Grandad built the Hideout together. On the day that it was finished Grandad presented Harry with a special book to store amongst his treasures.

'Harry,' he said. 'We have made a wonderful Hideout, but this book will teach you about the One who made the whole of the universe! Read it often.'

It was then that the adventures began …

Harry lay flat on his tummy at the edge of the pond, his head resting on his upturned hands. He had hardly moved from the same spot in the park all morning, peering out across the water, gazing in fascination at the tiny creatures moving across its surface.

Harry's brother, Joshua was busy playing football with some school friends on the grass nearby and, for once, Harry was glad that he had not been asked to join in.

'Harry!' Mum's voice broke the silence. 'Joshua's friend, Sam is coming home for lunch with us, so we need to leave in a minute.'

Harry jumped up, suddenly realising how hungry he was, and ran over to the bench where Mum was sitting enjoying the sunshine.

'Will you get the paddling pool out this afternoon?' he asked. 'Then I can see what I can get to float on the water like those creatures on the pond.'

'As long as it stays sunny,' agreed Mum. 'And as long as you don't make too big a mess … I remember the water fight you had last year,' she added, frowning at Harry and Joshua.

'We're bigger now,' Harry reassured her.

'Much more sensible,' Joshua added, smiling mischievously at Sam.

As soon as lunch was over Mum filled the paddling pool and Harry happily knelt by the side of it, testing to see if his toys would float or sink in the water. After a while Joshua and Sam appeared.

'What are you doing?' Joshua asked.

Harry explained about the creatures he had watched moving on the surface of the water earlier in the day.

'I bet you could do that,' Joshua told him.

'Do what?' asked Harry.

'Walk on the water like one of those creatures,' said Joshua.

Harry looked doubtful.

'You just need something to help you,' added Joshua. 'Wait a minute, I'll be back.'

Joshua ran inside and returned a few moments later with the large float that Harry used when they went swimming at the local pool.

'We'll hold it steady for you,' promised Joshua. 'And you climb on top of it and stand up. You'll be all right, we won't let go.'

Joshua and Sam each held one side of the float whilst Harry slowly lowered himself onto it, until he was sitting in the middle.

'Now stand up,' encouraged Joshua, pulling a face at Sam when Harry wasn't looking.

Harry eased himself round and pulled himself up into a crouching position. Slowly and carefully he stretched his knees. For one glorious moment he was balanced. Before …

SPLASH!

Harry fell backwards into the paddling pool, sending a fountain of water flying into the air.

Harry sat up immediately and wiped the water out of his eyes. Joshua and Sam were laughing hysterically, tears rolling down their faces.

Mum came running outside.

'Harry!' she shouted. 'What are you doing? Get inside now and get out of those wet clothes.'

'But … but, Mum,' Harry stammered. 'It was Joshua … he …'

'Harry, go inside!' Mum ordered. 'I told you not to make a mess and just look at you.'

As soon as Harry was changed into warm dry clothes he tiptoed back outside and snuggled down on a beanbag inside his Hideout. He felt silly and wanted to be on his own. Joshua was always playing tricks on him but it felt much worse when he did it in front of his friends. He didn't like being laughed at and he couldn't believe Mum was cross with him when it had all been Joshua's fault.

Harry looked round the Hideout wondering what to do. He spotted Grandad's special book. Carefully he reached up, lifted it down from the shelf and flicked through the pages. The title of a story caught his eye and Harry began to read …

Suddenly the Hideout began to spin. Harry felt tingles running through his body. He shut his eyes tight. This had happened before … Where would he end up this time?

When Harry first opened his eyes he could see nothing but darkness. The air felt cold and wet and the ground beneath him seemed to be rocking violently up and down. A sudden splash of cold water hit his face and Harry realised that he was seated at the back of a boat, behind a pile of fishing nets. He was dressed in a long brown tunic and a rough hooded cloak was wrapped tightly around his body. Harry shivered and tried to pull the cloak down over his bare feet.

Peering through the darkness, Harry could just make out the faint outline of some men frantically trying to keep the boat under control as the wind howled around them and waves battered them from every side. He was relieved that these seemed to be experienced fishermen.

Harry huddled against the nets hoping that they would provide some warmth and stared out across the water. It was then that he saw Him; a man was heading towards the boat, walking on the water! Harry's gasp was camouflaged by the shouts of the men. Everyone was terrified, until the man on the water spoke loudly above the noise of the wind.

'Don't be afraid. It's Me, Jesus.'

Almost at once Harry heard one of the men in the boat call out, 'Jesus, if it is You then tell me to come to You, walking on the water.'

Immediately Jesus replied, 'Yes, Peter, come to me.'

Harry held his breath. Surely Peter wasn't silly enough to actually get out of the boat. Surely he knew he would drown!

Peter sat on the edge of the boat and swung his legs over the side. Then, to Harry's amazement, Peter stood up and took a few steps towards Jesus. He was actually walking on the water! For a moment everything seemed fine but, as Harry watched, a look of fear began to spread over Peter's face. It was as if he suddenly realised that the wind was too strong and the waves were too big, and Peter began to sink down into the water.

'Help me!' he cried out.

Immediately Jesus moved forward and grabbed hold of Peter.

'Why did you doubt Me?' Harry heard Jesus ask, as He gently guided Peter back to the boat.

From where he was seated Harry could see the faces of both Jesus and Peter. Jesus wasn't laughing at him, nor was He angry. Instead His face showed a mixture of concern and care.

Harry looked at Peter. No longer did he look frightened; instead his face was full of amazement, as if he had suddenly realised something very special.

Jesus helped Peter to climb back on board the boat. Immediately the wind dropped and the boat began to bob calmly on the still water. Harry watched as the fishermen surrounded Jesus. Their faces were full of wonder; some of them knelt down and Harry heard them whisper, 'You really are the Son of God.'

Suddenly Harry felt tingles running through his body. Things began to spin. He shut his eyes tight …

When Harry opened his eyes he was back in his Hideout, Grandad's book resting on his knee. He sat still for a moment, thinking about what he had just seen. Peter had tried to walk on water, just like Harry had done earlier that day. Joshua and Sam had laughed at him and made him feel silly when he fell in and Mum had been cross with him. However, it had been different with Jesus. Jesus hadn't laughed at Peter nor had He been angry with him. Instead Jesus had lifted Peter out of the water and helped him back to safety. Jesus didn't seem to mind Peter making mistakes even if they were silly ones! Suddenly Harry felt much better.

He jumped up and ran back along the path towards the house. At the same time Joshua came charging out of the kitchen door. The two of them almost collided and, in his haste to move out of the way, Harry tripped over one of his toys and …

SPLASH!

Harry landed back in the paddling pool!

'Harry!' Mum's voice echoed out of the house. 'What was that noise?'

There was a moment of silence before both boys started to laugh!

Why not read this story in your own Bible? You will find it in Bible book Matthew, chapter 14 verses 22–33.

Have a go!

Small creatures can move over the surface of water because of something called the surface tension of water. Some liquids like washing-up liquid break the surface tension of water making it more difficult for tiny creatures to move on the surface. Why not try this experiment to see what happens?

You will need:

A tray of water, some washing-up liquid and a small boat shaped piece of paper (about 6cm x 2cm).

What to do:

With the help of a grown-up, fill the tray with water. The water doesn't need to be very deep – 1cm is plenty. Carefully place the boat about 2cm away from one end of the tray with the pointed end facing forward.

When the boat becomes still, place a small drop of washing-up liquid on the water directly behind the boat.

Watch to see what happens.

Because the surface tension of the water behind the boat has been broken, this experiment won't work more than once with the same water. To repeat the experiment you will need to empty the water, rinse the tray and fill with fresh water.